MOSE T's
SLAPOUT FAMILY ALBUM

Poems by Robert Ely

Paintings by Mose Tolliver

Essay by Julian Bond

Black Belt Press

These poems are dedicated with love

To my daughter, Elizabeth Vanessa Ely,

In fond memory of our many happy hours together in

The Bright Corner.

—R.E.

Library of Congress Cataloging-in-Publication Data is available.

Design by Breuna Baine
Printed in Hong Kong by Everbest Printing Company Ltd. through Four Colour Imports
96 97 98   5 4 3 2 1

The Black Belt Press, P.O. Box 551, Montgomery, AL 36101

The Black Belt, defined by its dark, rich soil, stretches across central Alabama. It was the heart of the cotton belt. It was and is a place of great beauty, of extreme wealth and grinding poverty, of pain and joy. Here we take our stand, listening to the past, looking to the future.

CONTENTS

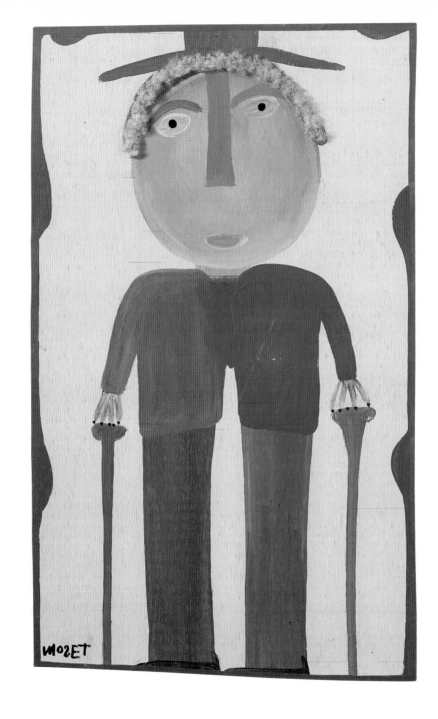

MOSE T.

Hello friend, and how-de-do!

This little book belongs to you!

And this whole world and all that's in it

Belong to you in every minute.

What lovely things there are to see

(Oh, by the way, my name's Mose T.)

If we just stop to look around

In our back yard, about the town,

Up in the sky, or at the flowers.

All of these good things are ours.

I made these pictures with real paint.

Folks often say they find them quaint.

But look right here! I'm tellin' you

Just what it is you ought to do.

The things you love, give them away,

Or sell them fair to those who pay.

These birds and turtles, snakes and fishes,

Have grown somehow from my own wishes.

And so I give them up to you.

Goodbye my friend, and how-de-do!

THE SLAPOUT FAMILY

There is a town called Slapout and
It's very dear to me,
And so it should be to you too
For its First Family.
They're famous creatures, great and small,
And happy as can be.
The Geek Bird and the Eagle fly,
The Buffalo, he swim.
Them Pylar Rattler got no bones.
(I'm glad that I'm not him!)
The Soft-Shelled Turtle takes the sun.
Diana Bird is prim.
There are so many creatures who
Live in the Slapout wood.
I wish that I might name them all,
Although I hardly could.
Yet there is one I can't forget
Because his song's so good.
The turtle folks call Porky Pine
Has justly earned renown.
In fact, his singing voice made him
The Mayor of the town!
And if you'll sing along with us
You'll never have to frown.

O O O O h h h h . . . .
Harumph ta diddle-da,
Harumph ta diddle-da,
Harumph ta diddle-da-do!
And I don't think I'd soon forget
Slapout if I were you!
No I don't think I'd soon forget
Slapout if I were you!

PORKY PINE TURTLE

Porky Pine Turtle got a name called Myrtle,
Got a wife got a name called Gus.
Saturday mornin', Gus wear her girdle,
And ride up high up on the trolley bus.
The trolley bus, the trolley bus,
She ride up high up on the trolley bus.
Ms. Turtle don't shop down Drury Lane,
She shop down Market Street.
Sometimes she lean up on her cane
And stop to rest her weary feet.
Her weary feet, her weary feet,
She stop to rest her weary feet.
Porky Pine Turtle chase down Gus Turtle;
She slap him with her cane.
Porky Pine Turtle, he grab her girdle;
Gus Turtle go back home again.
Back home again, back home again,
Gus Turtle go back home again!

PYLAR RATTLER

Them Pylar Rattler got no bones.

He slips and slides through mud and stones.

First slips this way, then slips that,

And on Sundays, wears a hat!

He slides to church up on his belly,

And if you ask him just how well he

Likes the preachin'—Look right here!

He wears a smile from ear to ear!

He sits up straight in his own pew.

Ask Preacher Owl, and he'll tell you

That when the ushers pass the plate

Old Pylar Rattler's never late

To pay the church more than he owes.

He doesn't dress in fancy clothes,

But spends his money doing good

For all the creatures in the wood.

Those folks who say he caused the Fall,

They don't know Pylar well at all.

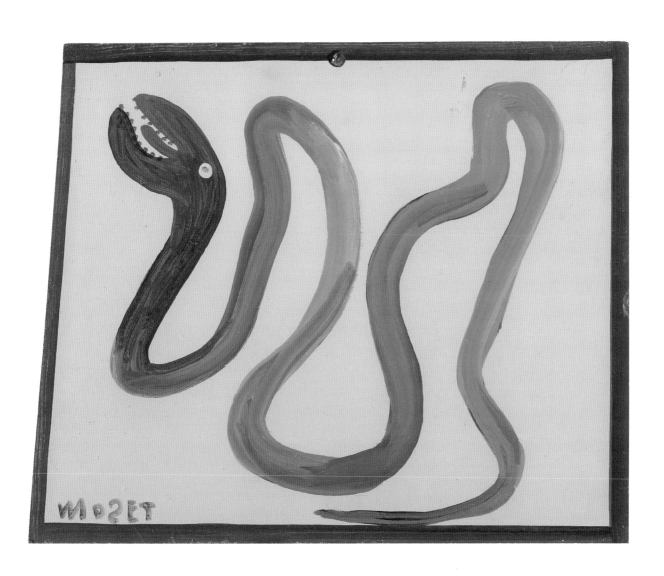

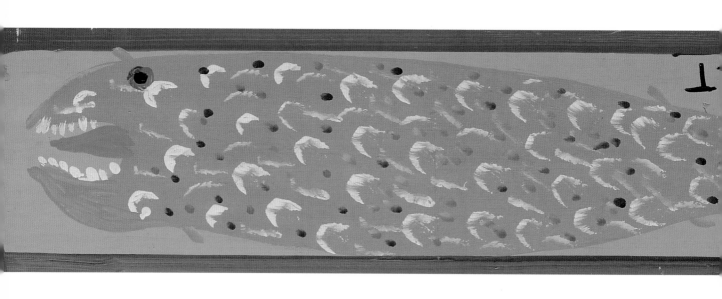

12

BUFFALO

The Buffalo, he's a sort-of fish,
The funniest fish that you ever could wish.
You'll never see him up on *my* dish,
Oh no, oh no,
Not the roly-o poly-o Buffalo!

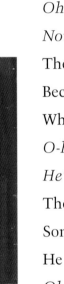

The Buffalo's got a big long tongue
Because of the many merry songs he's sung,
Which he began when he was young;
O-ho, O-ho,
He's the roly-o poly-o Buffalo!
The Buffalo live up in the lake
Some place beside the Pylar snake.
He won't eat nothin' but chocolate cake,
Oh no, oh no,
Not the roly-o poly-o Buffalo!
The Buffalo likes to sing this song,
And if you choose, you can sing along.
(He's no goldfish, don't get that wrong!)
Oh-no, Oh-no,
He's the roly-o poly-o Buffalo!

DIANIAN BIRD

Of the creature that's called the Dianian Bird
You will hear nothing bad, no not one single word.
In the world of bird gossip she's always immune
To the slanders of cads and the finch out of tune.
With her long flowing wings and her four-fingered toes
She's the picture of beauty wherever she goes.
Though she lives by herself up beside Slapout Wood,
Many gentlemen friends (whose intentions are good)
Bring her flowers and candy and sweetmeats and jewels,
But Dianian Bird always lives by her rules.
She's as chaste as creation the day it was made
And the envy of every feathery jade.

15

GEORGE WASHINGTON

George Washington, he's my kind of man,
He can build a new country fast as anyone can.
And when you want a first President,
He's the one to call, I say he's your gent.
George Washington, George Washington,
You sure made those Colonies a whole lot of fun!
George Washington, George Washington,
Oh won't you please come back and run?
Got a tall monument up in his own town,
Still the biggest prize of any President around.
Got a pretty little house down in Potomac woods
Filled with funky huntin' clothes and lots of fancy goods.
George Washington, George Washington,
You sure made those Colonies a whole lot of fun!
George Washington, George Washington,
Oh won't you please come back and run?
When I reach in my pocket for a one-dollar bill,
He's the man I'm goin' to see, and I always will.
The Father of our Country, he's still lookin' good,
And maybe it's because his teeth were made out of wood.
George Washington, George Washington,
You sure made those Colonies a whole lot of fun!
George Washington, George Washington,
Oh please, oh please come back and run!

THE TROLLEY BUS

Riding 'round the town of Slapout on the trolley bus

Is a famous lady turtle by the name of Gus.

Undiscouraged by the heat and high humidity

She departs the waiting room with no timidity.

When the driver takes her ticket then she's on her way

To another fine adventure on her shopping day

While the people all around her wonder "What is this?"

And their whispers slowly rise into a gentle hiss.

But she is not disturbed (for she knows she's not to blame)

That the people should remark upon her beauty and fame.

For she's known at Pike Road Center and Pine Apple too,

And of course when you are famous, well *what can you do*?

Riding 'round the town of Slapout on the trolley bus,

With a little luck Ms. Turtle might ride up with us!

EAGLE

The Eagle fly all day at night,
The Owl will tell you so.
The Eagle fly above the clouds
To hide from folks below.
Sometimes he fly above the stars,
A long, long way to go.
Sometimes at night he brings the wind,
Sometimes he brings the rain,
And when you hear a lonely sound,
Afar off like a train,
It might be Eagle flyin' by,
The wind up in his mane.
You'll never see the Eagle, no
I doubt you ever will.
For Eagle lives up by himself
And hides himself until
The night is dark, and you're asleep,
Asleep, asleep, asleep, asleep,
Asleep beneath the hill.

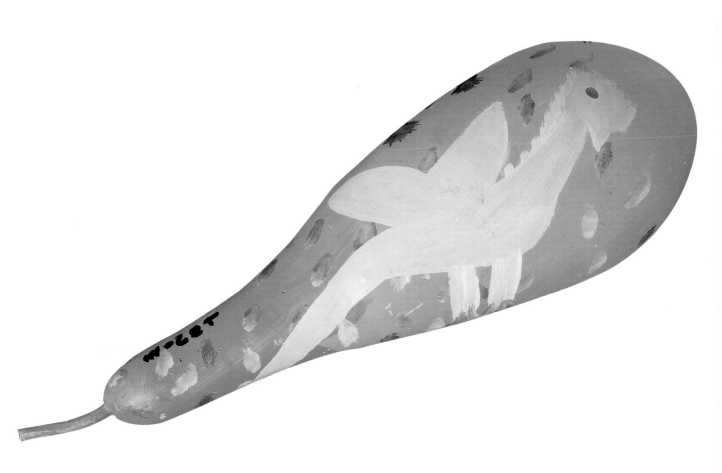

21

DRY BONES CHARLIE

Dry Bones Charlie he's made out of wood,
But he can dance much faster than you'd think he could,
With his drum-stick feet and his castanet toes
Soundin' clickity-clack wherever he goes.
Clickity-clack, clickity-clack,
Up and down the railroad track.
Clickity-clack, clickity-clack,
Dance to Baltimore and back!
Dry Bones Charlie's just a bundle of sticks.
He's got a banjo and a guitar he picks.
With his clothes pin fingers and that old banjo
You can hear him strummin' wherever he goes.
Strumedy-strum, strumedy-strum,
You can hear him go, you can hear him come.
Strumedy-strum, strumedy-strum,
And if you listen, you can hear him hum!
Dry Bones Charlie, don't you touch that match!
It's got something on it that you might catch!
And if you should, I say if you should,
You'd be very very sorry that you're made out of wood!
Made out of wood, made out of wood,
You'd be very very sorry that you're made out of wood!

23

SOFT-SHELLED TURTLE

The Soft-Shelled Turtle's life's not hard.

He takes the sun out in his yard

And when he likes, goes for a swim.

I find I often envy him,

For he can swim in his own lake.

His life's a great big piece of cake!

He doesn't fear his mother's wrath

If he avoids his nightly bath

Since he is always squeaky clean,

The cleanest turtle ever seen

About the town, where he's well known.

His girlfriends call him on the phone

To ask if he'll go on a date.

When they arrive, he makes them wait,

But they don't even seem to mind

Or find him in the least unkind.

He has his fun, and it's for sure,

He's Slapout's number one flaneur!

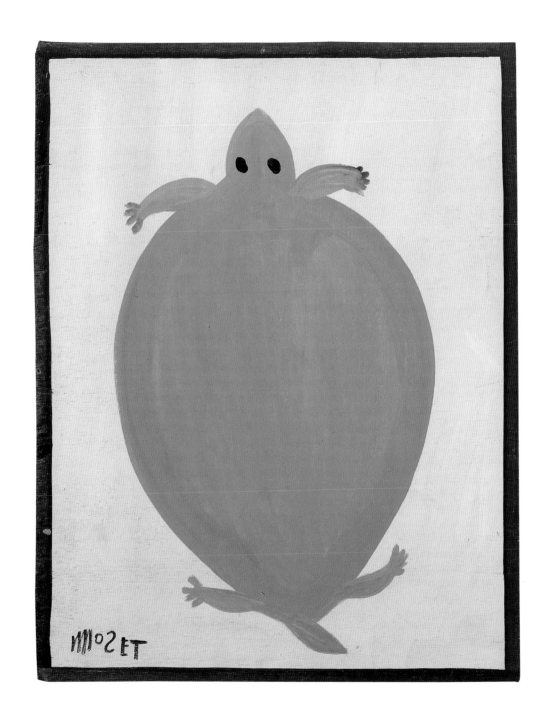

25

THE GEEK BIRD

The Geek Bird lives in Slapout Town,
And he goes to the Slapout School,
Where he learns to know his verb from his noun
And to fly by the Golden Rule.
(But what the Geek Bird does the best
Is not his elocution test!)
Sometimes the Geek Bird sleeps in class,
And sometimes he's not good.
And every night he prays that he'll pass,
And he daily knocks on wood.
(For he knows what he does the best
Is not his long division test!)
When Master Owl says, "Class dismissed,"
The Geek Bird flies away,
And on this one thing I'll insist
Until my dying day,
That what the Geek Bird does the best
He does when class has been recessed!

QUAIL FISH

The Quail Fish live up in a tree
And swim in Slapout wood.
That's rather odd, don't you agree?
(I really think you should.)
Yet living there he feels quite free
And finds the swimming good.
The Quail Fish, the Quail Fish,
He is most truly what you wish!
Of course I've read of fish that fly
(And squirrels too, you know)
Yet I've not seen one flying by
From where I stand below.
Perhaps the Quail Fish fly too high?
(I guess I'll never know.)
The Quail Fish, the Quail Fish,
He is most truly what you wish!
Now I've been asked by Master Owl,
About this Quail Fish,
Just whether he be fish or fowl,
And I say, "What you wish!"
On this I will not waste a vowel!
He's just a Quail Fish!
The Quail Fish, the Quail Fish,
He is most truly what you wish!

29

WHAT IT IS

The naming of pictures is not all that easy.
It isn't a thing that we do every day.
In fact it might cause us to feel a bit queasy,
Unless we can make it a matter of play.
Let's take, for example, a picture of something
That's sticky and sweet and delightful to chew.
We might call that picture *A Joyful Galumphing*,
But that would mean nothing to me or to you.
It is what it is, oh it is what it is,
And there is no name at all like what it is!
Of course this fine picture must have its own title.
There certainly can be no doubt about that.
A name for this picture is really quite vital,
And yet we most clearly can't call it *A Hat*.
It's not what it isn't, it is what it is,
And there is no name at all like what it is!
A name for this picture is what we are after,
A properly wonderful name that is true.
And though we might call it *A Red Lambogaster*,
I really don't think such a name would quite do.

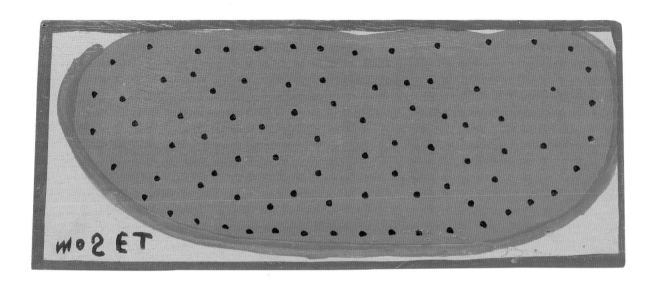

It is what it is, oh it is what it is,

And there is no name at all like what it is!

Of course we might call it *A Fresh Watermelon,*

And people would know what we meant in Cadiz.

Yet we are not trying to please Dick and Helen,

And so to "What is it?" we'll say, "What It Is!"

It's not what it isn't, it is what it is,

And there is no name at all like What It Is!

SWAYBACK HORSE

Clippita-cloppita,
Bandy-legged Swayback Horse
Been around Slapout Town
Since time began.
Looks most incredible,
Unpedigreeable!
Still I confess I'm his
Number one fan!
Clippita-cloppita,
Bandy-legged Swayback Horse
Works real hard, eats his hay,
Does the same every day.
I have one question
Prosoequestrian:
How did he save such a
Huge IRA?

33

THE JICK-JACK

The Jick-Jack, she's a dancin' girl.

She might be Sally, or she might be Pearl.

She likes to spin, and she likes to twirl.

She's a dancin', twirlin' Jick-Jack girl!

And when she spins, her skirt flies out.

That's what a Jick-Jack's all about.

She makes the folks stand up and shout.

She's a Jick-Jack girl, beyond a doubt.

The Jick-Jack soon kicks off her shoes

When she begins to feel the blues.

Her partners, they line up in queues.

She's a dancin' girl you can't refuse.

She likes to dance with Billy-Jill.

He loves her true, and he always will.

She dances with her Bill until

They're Billy-Jack and Billy-Jill!

The Jick-Jack, she's a dancin' girl.

She might be Sally, or she might be Pearl.

She likes to spin, and she likes to twirl.

She's a dancin', twirlin' Jick-Jack girl!

HOODOO MAN

A man lives in the forest who
Folks call the Slapout Hoodoo Man.
He's not at all like me or you.
He learned his art from Kubla Khan.
Oh yes, the Hoodoo Man is crafty.
The Hoodoo Man works on the sly.
His house is in a cave that's drafty
With bugs and bats that creep and fly.
And should you take a chilly walk
Beside his cave some autumn night,
You just might hear some Hoodoo talk
Or see an eerie spirit light.
Yes, when the autumn moon is full
And shadows thick upon the ground,
His chants become quite audible,
And you can hear this dreadful sound:
Munkaja-bunkaja fundimalorum,
Pinkaja-pankaja dunkaladee,
Doomina-domina haja decorum,
Splishida-splashida fol-dol-re-mi!
But do not be too frightened, no,
Don't think the Hoodoo Man is mean.
He does his little magic show
To tell the world it's Halloween!

37

THE SLAPOUT CHRISTMAS TREE

On the night before Christmas, inside Slapout Wood
All the creatures are happy that they have been good,
For this is the night all await with such glee,
The night when Saint Nick visits *their* Christmas tree!
Oh the presents he'll bring! and the fun they'll enjoy,
As each creature opens a book or a toy!
(And what do you think all these friends will receive?
There's something quite special for each, I believe.
And Santa Claus told me that I might tell you.
But you mustn't tell *them*! Oh no, that wouldn't do!)
The Dianian Bird is the first on the list.
There's a diamond necklace for her, I insist!
And the Rattler called Pylar gets what he wants most,
A black leather Bible and jelly for toast.
Gus Turtle will also be pleased, I've no doubt,
That Santa has got her a rocker for gout!
The Eagle and Geek Bird each want a bright horn,
And each will receive one upon Christmas morn.
The roly-o poly-o Buffalo wishes
That Santa will bring him a set of toy dishes,
So that's what he'll get, and of that I am sure,
While a violet cumberbund, oh so demure,
Will be wrapped and awaiting the glad Soft-Shelled Turtle.
But what of that Porky Pine Turtle called Myrtle?

Oh what will our jolly friend Santa bring him?
I will tell you the truth (for its not just my whim).
A red turtle bicycle, tied with a bow,
Is waiting for Porky Pine! *Ho ho ho ho!*

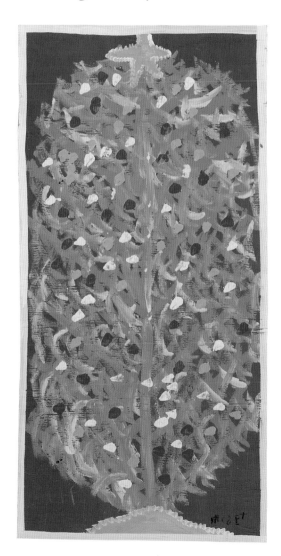

BLACK JESUS

See? There are no nails that can hold me.

No, the dove wing of death can't enfold me.

And no one can my image capture.

None know me well until their rapture

Turns each breath into devotion.

You must put off your sense and notion.

The highest wisdom's often simple:

See how the morning waters wimple!

Do not delight in complex theory,

For in the end, your soul grows weary.

You see, I'm found with birds and fishes

And not some thought folks wills or wishes.

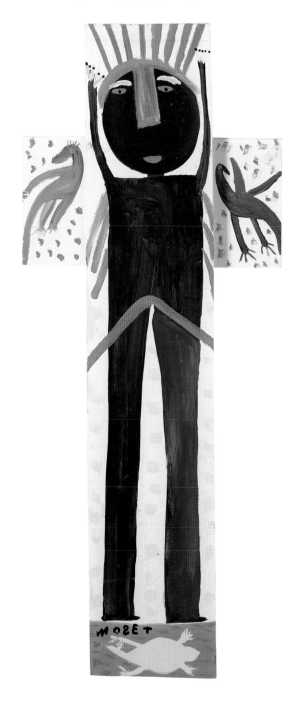

41

STAR-FLOWER

To all of God's creatures, so glad in the sun,

To the fish in the lakes and the birds in the sky,

The bright-burning star and the flower are one.

The world is a place where the day's never done,

Where darkness and clouds do not stay, but pass by,

To all of God's creatures, so glad in the sun.

To the child whose sweet life has only begun,

Who yet has not tasted regret or a sigh,

The bright-burning star and the flower are one.

The summer is green; there are races to run,

And turtles to catch and ice-cream to buy

To all of God's creatures so glad in the sun.

Now the point of this poem is life is such fun

It's silly for you or for me to ask why

To all of God's creatures, so glad in the sun,

The bright-burning star and the flower are one!

43

Meet Mr. Mose Tolliver

by Julian Bond

Mose Tolliver is an American artist, born on the 4th of July, about 1920.

He is also a "folk" artist, a "primitive" artist, a "self-taught" artist, a "vernacular" artist, a "naive" artist, and a "subconscious" artist.

These terms are variously applied to artists like Mose Tolliver. Unlike many of those artists, Tolliver's paintings have attracted international attention.

I have never asked Tolliver how he would describe himself, but I suspect he would use one word—"artist" or "painter."

I visited his Montgomery, Alabama, home a few years ago, bearing a four-foot high wooden plant stand I wanted him to paint.

"How much will this cost?" I asked him.

"I don't know," he replied. "It depends on how much art it takes."

His art takes me and countless others to new levels of expression.

He is part of—and partly responsible for—a modern explosion in appreciation of artists like him, many of them sharing his biography—black, Southern, without formal training, frequently instructed to paint or sculpt or create by dreams, visions, or messages from God.

Mose Tolliver's art can now be found everywhere—from floor to ceiling in his own home, on the gallery-like walls of the homes of wealthy collectors, in museums worldwide, decorating a chain of blues nightclubs, and in the homes of people who don't fancy themselves as knowledgeable partisans of any form of art.

Robert Ely and Mose Tolliver at Mr. Tolliver's home-studio-gallery.

His work speaks to those who love it. Like Tolliver himself, it is accessible—immediately striking a responsive chord.

Tolliver came to painting late in life. The child of sharecroppers in rural Montgomery County, Alabama, he dropped out of school at any early age. In the 1960s, while he was working at a Montgomery furniture company, some sheets of marble fell on his legs, permanently disabling him.

His employer, who painted as a hobby, encouraged Tolliver to take up painting in his forced retirement, and using house paint on pasteboard, he painted a red bird.

"After that, I painted birds for two

or three years 'cause I didn't know nothin' else to paint," he has said.[1]

Tolliver has not lacked for subjects since then, but he also returns to themes repeatedly, refining and redefining them—his early watermelons are much prized now, but subtly different from the watermelons a visitor to his home or a New York gallery might see today.

Even if the theme is the same, each one of Tolliver's birds and watermelons and moose ladies is different, and each places him at the pinnacle of American art.

His art appeals to a long-standing American egalitarianism, the notion that but for trying, I could do that. But it also signals to us that we really could not, that here before us is a rare genius, someone who does what we cannot possibly do—puts on canvas (or on Mose Tolliver's boards) a vision of things we do not see and had not imagined until the artist showed them to us. Then all becomes clear.

Much of his art is autobiographical. He produces paintings of himself, standing with two canes; of his late wife, Willie Mae; and his daughter, Annie, herself an artist of growing reputation.

All of it is simple—not easily done or uncomplicated, but transparently guileless in the ease in which it approaches us and we see it, elementary and self-explanatory, mysteriously ingenious and unpretentious all at once.

You can lose yourself in Mose Tolliver's world and, through his art, find your way home.

Writer, lecturer, and commentator Julian Bond is a history professor at the University of Virginia. He was a co-founder of the Student Non-Violent Coordinating Committee and for many years served in the Georgia state legislature.

[1]"Mose Tolliver" in *Revelations,* text by Kathy Kemp (Birmingham: Crane Hill Publishers, 1994).

Major Exhibitions

The paintings of Mose Tolliver have been exhibited in dozens of significant art shows at museums and galleries throughout the United States and elsewhere. His work is included in the permanent collections of the National Museum of American Art (Washington), the Museum of American Folk Art (New York), the Milwaukee Art Museum, the Birmingham Art Museum, and many others. Some of his more important exhibitions have included *Black Folk Art in America: 1930-1980* at the Corcoran Gallery of the Smithsonian Museum (1982), *Passionate Visions of the American South: Self-Taught Artists from 1940 to the Present* at the New Orleans Museum of Art (1993), and a one-man show at the Montgomery Museum of Fine Art (1981).

Selected Bibliography

Brackner, Joey, and Tom Patterson. *Outsider Artists in Alabama*. Montgomery: Alabama State Council on the Arts, 1991.

Johnson, Jay, and William C. Ketchum, Jr. *American Folk Art of the Twentieth Century*. New York: Rizzoli, 1993.

Kemp, Kathy. *Revelations: Alabama's Visionary Folk Artists*. Birmingham: Crane Hill, 1994.

Livingston, Jane, and John Beardsley. *Black Folk Art in America: 1930-1980*. Jackson: Mississippi University Press, 1982.

Rosenak, Chuck, and Jan Rosenak. *Museum of American Folk Art Encyclopedia of Twentieth-Century American Folk Art and Artists*. New York: Abbeville, 1990.

University of Southwestern Louisiana Art Museum. *Baking in the Sun: Visionary Images from the South*. Lafayette: SW Louisiana University Press, 1987.

Contributors

From the collection of Micki Beth Stiller:

Mose Tolliver, Self-portrait, 20" x 32", house paint on plywood, 1984, p. 4; The Slapout Family (after a painting by Bill Traylor), 20" x 20", house paint on plywood, 1993, p. 7; George Washington, 24" x 24", house paint on plywood, 1982, p. 17; Trolley Bus, 32" x 16.5", house paint on plywood, 1987, p. 19; Dry Bones Charlie, 11.5" x 16.5", house paint on plywood, 1981, p. 23; Watermelon, 20.5" x 8.5", house paint on plywood, 1982, p. 31; Swayback Horse, 6.5" x 12", house paint on plywood, 1989, p. 33; Hoodoo Man, 10" x 19", house paint on plywood, 1990, p. 37; Black Jesus, 16" x 40", house paint on plywood, 1984, p. 41.

From the collection of Georgine and Jack Clarke:

Pylar Rattler, 18" x 15", house paint on plywood, 1992, p. 11.

From the collection of Marcia Webber Art Objects:

Quail Fish, 39" x 12", house paint on plywood, 1985, p. 28-29.

From the collection of Becky and Bill Cumbie:

Slapout Christmas Tree, 24" x 48", house paint on plywood, 1988, p. 39.

From the collection of Mr. and Mrs. Robert Ely:

Porky Pine Turtle, 19" x 22.5", house paint on plywood, 1990, p. 9; Buffalo, 21.5" x 5.5", house paint on wood, 1991, p. 12-13; Dianian Bird, 21" x 19.5", house paint on plywood, 1991, p. 15; Eagle, circumference 19", length 20.5", house paint on a gourd, 1990, p. 21; Soft-Shelled Turtle, 18" x 23.5", house paint on plywood, 1985, p. 25; Geek Bird, 7.5" x 8", house paint on plywood, 1988, p. 27; The Jick-Jack, 17" x 25", house paint on plywood, 1990, p. 35; Star-Flower, 6" x 5", house paint on Masonite, 1989, p. 43.

All dates are approximate.